Your Journey of Transformation:

~A Workbook for a New You~

By

Tiza Pyle, PhD

This book is dedicated to

CHANGE

And to all courageous people who have already embraced it,
or who are willing to embrace it now.

Your Journey of Transformation

~A Workbook for a New You~

Disclaimer

This book is designed to provide helpful information on the subjects addressed. The author and publisher disclaim all liability associated with the recommendations and guidelines set forth here. It is sold with the understanding that the author and publisher's only objective is to provide information and support to those choosing to make changes in their lives.

If the change you are contemplating involves any health, or complex financial or legal issues, please consult your personal advisors to ensure that your plan is sound. You should rely on your physician's advice regarding the appropriate choice of strategy for your diet, weight loss and/or other health related goals.

References are provided for informational purposes only and do not constitute endorsement of any websites or other sources.

ISBN 978-0-9982289-2-1

Pyle Consulting Group, Inc.

TABLE OF CONTENTS

INTRODUCTION

Your Journey of Transformation: A Workbook for a New You is a "how to" practical approach to help you make changes and transform your life! Yes, I believe transformation is possible as we open ourselves to possibilities and to what we really want in life – our true aspirations.

For me, change is exciting. It offers a world of opportunities and the possibility for growth; and that sort of personal development requires change. I understand, however, that you may not find the change process to be so exciting. You may be motivated by your vision of the end result, but not the path to achieving it. And this is why ***Your Journey of Transformation: A Workbook for a New You*** has been created: to help you navigate your personal change with confidence.

Change may not be comfortable, and at times not desired, but when you can recognize its positive power for growth and renewal, change becomes the key to a more meaningful life. Mother Nature changes and renews constantly, and we need to follow Her path to remain viable and present in this world. Some changes are small and hidden, but these are happening every day. However, meaningful change happens only when we embrace the value of a different reality. At this stage of my life, I want to share what I have learned – through successes and failures.

Only you can transform your life, even in the midst of unwanted change.
No one else can do it, no matter how hard they try!

The secret of successful change is found in three basic steps:

First: Awareness – something is not right, and you do not like what is going on. It could be you are not as effective as you could be, relationships are not what you expect, the job brings you no satisfaction, and the list goes on. Being aware that "something is not right" is the first step towards a different reality.

Second: Acceptance – becoming fully accountable for the current situation and knowing that you need to do something different to achieve another outcome.

Third: Action (taking concrete steps for change) – creating new patterns of thinking and behaving that are in line with your new desired reality.

These three elements are present in any type of change. And YOU can make the changes you want!

This workbook will walk you through a way to better understand where you are in your change process and to develop a plan to reach a new reality, your desired new future.

Usually, when change is being considered, it is easier to talk about the **reasons (why)** something has to be different and **what** will be changed. Perhaps these are easier steps, as they do not deal with the actual process of change. However, the **HOW** is more challenging. **Results are in the execution of your plan**. Strategy and planning are the start, but are not enough. To achieve what you want to accomplish, a plan is an essential step for success.

Another lesson I learned from experience is that flexibility and openness are key to a happier and more productive life.

This quote from Confucius has always been a favorite:

> *"The green reed which bends in the wind is stronger than the mighty oak which breaks in a storm."*

You may know, or have experienced working with someone with a very rigid approach, and have seen the price paid by many who cannot change and adapt to a new reality. The results of such behavior can create many difficulties for the person and those around them. However, if you can look at changes in your life as opportunities, you can create a new reality that is positive, empowering and even fun!

This workbook has been created for you and provides a private space where you can explore your readiness for any change, the stages that are normal in the personal change process and a simple but powerful tool to create a plan for your success. It is work, but the rewards are well worth the effort – and you can do it!

I wish you peace, joy and great success in creating the future you want.

Dr. Tiza Pyle, PhD

Chapter 1 – The Start of Your Journey

The Challenge of Personal Transformation

> *"All changes, even the most longed for, have their melancholy;*
> *for what we leave behind us is a part of ourselves;*
> *we must die to one life before we can enter another."*
> Anatole France

When you read this quote, what comes to your mind?

____

____

____

____

____

____

____

____.

There are times change is seen as a negative, and "even the most longed for" comes with a price. Once you can accept this, you have taken the first step towards real transformation: becoming a different version of who you are now.

We hear a lot about the pros and cons for change, whether to change or not change – articles come at us regularly on this subject. *"Can people really change?"* is the question I hear perhaps most frequently. As a coach I do believe personal transformation is possible, but my response to the questions about ability to change, usually, is both *yes*, and *no*! You may say, "That's not very helpful, Dr. Tiza." But here is my thinking on this topic.

First, the YES.

I say "yes" to change because I firmly believe that people have the ability to modify behaviors, habits and patterns of thinking that are no longer effective in their current life. You have the power to develop and the opportunity to grow in ways you may not realize in order to reach your full potential. You can transform your life and reinvent yourself many times to achieve what you want and what is important to you. I've done it – I've created a system for it – and I will show you how.

Now, the NO.

I say "no" to change because I have observed that our basic personality traits are well established at a very early age. Many of these traits are hard wired in our brains; and many of them are beyond our ability for easy change. Recognizing this fact is also important for growth and development.

However, self-awareness and a firm desire to modify your current mindset and develop new habits – and, being ready to work at it, are the key ingredients for overriding this circuitry and achieving the transformational success you desire.

You can conquer many of the challenges that are part of change with a better understanding of the processes and an openness to new opportunities in your life. If you embrace the personal transformation process, it can be extremely rewarding – and fun!

When you think about change, keep in mind that –

- Change is inevitable.
- Change is essential for growth and development.
- Change is not easy!

As you start on your journey of change, whether big or small, another important factor for success is having a reliable road map: *If you do not know where you want to go, any road will lead you to nowhere.* And this is particularly true for the process of personal transformation.

You will discover that *change management* principles will be at the core of your work with transformation. What I offer you in this workbook comes from lessons learned from my corporate work, my formal education and my own personal experience. The goal is to help you develop a deeper understanding of the personal change process, and to offer some suggestions on strategies you can use to make your process less stressful and more fun and successful.

It is somewhat easy to understand why resistance to any new idea remains a strong presence in our lives. Here are the main reasons for this:

- When any change is introduced, or suggested, it challenges the beliefs we have held for many years.

- You have a strong commitment to who you are now, what you do and know (your profession, knowledge, lifestyle, etc.)

- It is more comfortable to remain in the *known*, rather than risk the *unknown* in our lives. And change represents this leap into a new, untested reality.

Change involves discomfort and apprehension. This is why ***the pain of not changing has to be greater than the pain of changing.*** Getting yourself to take a good look at the consequences of "not changing" is part of the challenge you face. Ultimately, it is a very personal choice and one that only you can make!

One of the lessons to be learned as you embark on the process of change is to know that new ideas and concepts take a long time to emerge and change. In a way, these new ideas are challenging the reality that you have known for many years: concepts and ideas that are familiar and comfortable for you and those around you. The same is true for your habits and way of doing things.

Also, you need to know that your personal transformation will not make you someone you were not before. Transformation is the process of modifying, of sculpting – not of recreating. You are whole and valuable, and your desire for change is a way to find what you really want in your life, and what is important to you. Embrace the idea that change is an evolutionary process, and not a revolutionary one. And understand that it takes time and sustained effort. You will need to believe that you can do it, successfully!

How to Use This Workbook

This workbook has been structured to help you reflect and to give you enough space to record your discoveries. You will find many questions and exercises that I hope will stimulate your thinking, challenge your current assumptions, and open the way to explore new possibilities.

There are no "right" or "wrong" answers. This is about *you*: your current reality, and what you want to create for your future.

Consider taking time to answer the questions, to go deeper in your thinking and feelings in order to make this exploration more meaningful and useful to you. "Peel the onion" without fear to get to the core of what matters to you most in your new desired reality. This is your private space of exploration.

You will find in the workbook information and exercises covering the following:

The ***B.A.S.E. Model for Change***, with its 4 pillars:

- Belief
- Acceptance
- Support
- Execution

An Introduction to Transitions: The Personal Side of Change. Knowing and accepting predictable internal changes you experience as responses to external changes. Embracing the process of transition in your personal change journey will allow you to move forward, with confidence.

An Exploration of Readiness for Change is included as a step in the ***B.A.S.E. Model for Change***. This is an important element in any personal change, particularly those that include changing long standing habits.

Having a specific situation in mind will help you focus on the desired outcome and facilitate your work in the process. Thus, think about a change you are planning, or are already experiencing now.

Some examples of change situations people experience are listed below. Each one of these can be challenging and may create the need to reinvent yourself, and your life! You may identify with one or more in this list or have another that best fits your current reality.

- Moving into a new neighborhood/city
- Losing your current job
- Starting a new job
- Losing a spouse
- Creating a healthier lifestyle through exercise and nutrition
- Considering retirement or being retired
- Planning to "downsize" and leave your home
- Children leaving for college
- Illness or becoming a caregiver
- Other:______________________

Selecting one situation to start using this workbook will not limit you, as you can repeat the process for other changes, as you become familiar with the questions and exercises suggested.

At any time when you decide to embark on your journey of change and transformation, an important step towards success is to find that "compelling reason" that will motivate and support you during the difficult times in this process. As it has been mentioned earlier, change is not easy and will take work – but you can do it. The questions in each section in this workbook will guide you in creating a road map to your new reality.

You may consider finding a partner or a coach to work with you during this process. Having an accountability "buddy" can help you stay on track and reach your desired outcome.

In order to create your new reality, you need to be ready to work, but also to find enjoyment in the process. This is about you, your future, and your happiness. The questions in the workbook have been created to challenge your thinking and help you along the way of long-term and sustainable transformation. It is work that brings fulfillment and hopefully a sense of peace and accomplishment.

Are you ready to start this new journey? On the following page you will find space to identify your change and your compelling reason.

I wish you great success, and a joyful adventure of self-discovery!

Your Transformation Journey

Describe in a few words what you want to change (or the change you are already experiencing.) This workbook will help you create and implement a plan for your desired future.____

____

____

____

____

____.

Now, in the space below, list the major reasons why this change is important to you. Once this is done, identify the reason that is the most important to you, the one that will give you the motivation needed to reach your goal. This becomes your compelling reason for change.

____

____

____

____

____

____

____

____

Chapter 2 – The B.A.S.E. Model for Change

How This Model was Created

The ***B.A.S.E. Model for Change*** is a result of reflecting on my own life experience and the many life transformations I was able to make with a good degree of success!

Sharing my experience is a way of suggesting a path you also can follow to successfully navigate changes in your life. And, in using this model, I ask that you do not look for perfection, but what is "good enough" to make you happy!

Looking back at my own life, I see some major changes, and I think that if you reflect in your history, you will find similar experiences. For me the changes that have been more significant in my adult life include:

- Moving from Brazil to the US to get married in my early twenties,
- Changing jobs several times to better meet my professional goals,
- Going back to school to earn a master's degree when my children were teen-agers,
- Moving to another city with my husband in my mid-fifties,
- Selling and buying houses, and moving several times,
- Completing my PhD when I was almost 60,
- Losing over 130 pounds in my mid-sixties, and keeping it off,

- Starting a consulting practice after I retired.

These were the major ones until recently!

So, one question I have asked myself is "what have I done to survive and thrive through all these changes?"

From this personal exploration and the hard questions I have asked myself, the ***B.A.S.E. Model for Change*** was born. Reflecting on my own experiences, I realized that I had used the steps I describe here many times, in an instinctive way, and without being fully aware that this really represented an organized process.

After this discovery and knowing that this model can work in times of difficult changes, I decided to share my experience and create this workbook so you would also be able to develop your own roadmap for your journey of transformation.

And, in early 2019, as I was completing this work, I found myself in the midst of still another difficult change: dealing with my husband's failing health, becoming his primary caregiver and moving into a retirement community. This time I was very mindful of the importance of the steps in the ***B.A.S.E. Model for Change***, as I was going through the change process. The model works, it is not easy, but it is worth the effort!

I have survived another major change using the model! And I trust you will also find this useful as you contemplate your journey through changes.

For many, change can be challenging and difficult – I fully understand this! For others, change can be fun and full of opportunities. However, no matter how you see change, remember that what you know – your current reality – is comfortable and safe and the new and unknown can be daunting. Having some structure to help you navigate the uncertainty of a new reality is helpful. The ***B.A.S.E. Model for Change*** is your road map. Use it to create a safe path to your new reality.

Steps in the B.A.S.E. Model for Change

You will find the ***B.A.S.E. Model for Change*** is a very practical process that can be used in many types of life changes. It encompasses 4 broad categories with some guiding principles under each one.

Here is the definition of each letter in the model:

B – Belief – having the confidence that you can do something different in your life.

A – Awareness – taking the time to learn about who you are, what you will need to change to make your process successful, and accepting who you really are – all of it.

S – Support – opening yourself to ask for and accept the help you will need to ensure the success of the change, both people and processes.

E – Execution – creating a plan that is customized to you and leads to the result you want. Results only come when you actually do something to reach your desired new reality.

This is a simple, but powerful model – the practical **How To** – that can allow you to write your own story and reinvent yourself as many times as you want, **being YOUR best in each stage of your life**. However, being simple does not mean that it will not take work and focus on your part. And you can use this model as many times as you need, and have the rewarding feeling of having succeeded one more time in your quest to a **new you.**

A few thoughts as you embark on this journey:

- The first step – Belief is probably the hardest one, as it will ask you to develop a clear picture of your desired future, find a compelling reason for this change, and challenge your readiness for this change. It is a first necessary step in your journey of personal transformation.

- Some changes will be easier, such as moving into a new neighborhood, changing jobs, starting a new project. But making long-lasting changes in behaviors such as stop smoking, changing addictive behaviors, reaching a healthy weight are much harder and will require significant work, time and perhaps additional professional support.

- As you work on Awareness, remember that there are no "right or wrong" answers. This section is intended to help you gain a deeper knowledge and acceptance of who you are, and what you really want.

You will be asked to answer many suggested questions and reflect on topics that you can use in support of your personal change process. As you work the various stages of the ***B.A.S.E. Model for Change***, make the time to reflect and use this workbook as your safe space to explore the challenges before you.

By thinking of this model in a purposeful way you will discover that once incorporated in your thinking process, it can be repeated many times, with very positive outcomes. Think of the model as the foundation for success in your personal transformation plan.

BELIEF

> *Once you make a decision, the universe conspires to make it happen.*
> Ralph Waldo Emerson

I like quotes, and this one above makes a lot of sense and provides focus on what you will be asked to do in this portion of the workbook.

The first step in the ***B.A.S.E. Model for Change*** is Belief – your internal force that drives you to create the reality that you want. This first step has some key elements that will help you in this process. These are described below:

- **Mindset – developing a winning approach and believing in yourself "I can do this."**
- **Vision – knowing where you want to go and be.**
- **Compelling reason – having an objective strong enough to sustain you during the difficult process of changing habits and behaviors.**
- **Being ready for change – recognizing the challenges of the process.**

The questions on the following pages are designed to help you have faith in yourself to reach your aspirations, create a clear picture of what you want, explore potential barriers for change and identify your compelling reason for change.

There aren't any "right or wrong" answers! This is a tool to help you organize your thoughts and clearly identify what you want to achieve. Allow yourself some time to think about the questions and record your answers in this book. It has been designed to become a useful road map for your journey. Again, there are no right or wrong answers, just an honest exploration of your real aspirations. And you can do it!

Mindset: Developing a Winning Approach

Believing in yourself is at the core of creating a mindset that moves you forward. In this context:

- Mindset doesn't apply only to the functionality of your brain – your rational self – but to the connection of mind, heart and spirit and its power to motivate you and help you design and achieve the life you desire.

- Mindset also includes the ability to recognize the importance of living one day at a time, in the present, without the anxiety of worrying about the past – that you cannot change, and the future – that you cannot control, but that you can design.

- A positive mindset can provide the environment necessary to create a reality that fulfills your dreams and potential while bringing you peace and joy. It gives you the confidence to get it done.

Please complete the questions below:

What is my track record, so far, when I decide to make a change?

____

____

____

____

____

____

____

____.

What has allowed me to be successful, when I accomplished a difficult goal?

____

____

____

____

____

____

____

____.

How can I create space in my life for meaningful exploration of what I want to do and who I want to become?

____

____

____

____

____

____

____

____.

What are my present self-limiting thoughts that can or will impact my success?

____

What self-affirming thoughts I will need to develop to help me reach my goals?

____

Creating your Vision: Declaring your Dream

> *Your vision will become clear only when you can look into your own heart.*
> *Who looks outside, dreams, who looks inside, awakes.*
>
> Carl Jung

You need a clear vision of what you want to create in your future. Below are a few ideas on how to develop your vison for the future you want. This can become the story of what you want to be and do with your life, and the opportunity to make this new reality bold and wonderful. Look into your heart and think big!

Find a quiet space and allow yourself to relax and imagine what you really want from your life. Take your time to create a meaningful picture, including details, and how you are feeling with this new reality you are creating. It may be helpful to use pictures rather than only words during this process. Have fun designing your future!

Use the questions below to guide you in your journey of creating the vision of your new reality.

Where do you want to be in 2, 5 or 10 years? Identify your timeframe and create a picture of your physical space.

____

____

____

____

____

____.

What do you want to be doing? Think about the activities you enjoy and describe these in some detail. How do you feel doing these activities?

____

____

____

____

____

____

____

____.

Who is involved in your life: are you single, in a relationship, with children, empty nesting, retired, with a partner, living in another city/country, or many others?

____

____

____

____

____

____

____

____.

What other activities are you involved in?

____

What are your hobbies?

What quality of life do you wish to enjoy?

If you are able to contribute to a cause or interest, what is your choice and expand on the reason for it.

Finding your Compelling Reason

> *"You may be disappointed if you fail, but you are doomed if you don't try."*
> Beverly Sills

Changes in your life that bring satisfaction and fulfilment are those that are made for a reason that is important to you. This key reason needs to be very clear in your mind and heart. Only then, you will be able to plan and succeed in achieving your desired new reality. At the start of this workbook you listed various reasons for your desired change.

Now it is time to select that all important reason, the one above all the others, that started you in this process. This powerful goal – your compelling reason for change – becomes the anchor that will support and sustain you in your journey of transformation.

As you begin this journey into the new reality you want to create, I invite you to answer the following questions relative to your change. Answer them honestly as you create your blueprint for successful change. Recording your thoughts about the process can be very helpful and give you an opportunity to gauge your progress.

> *Having a compelling reason for your transformation process is a key element of success.*
> *Finding yours will give you the needed motivation for success.*

Allow yourself some time to think about the following questions and record your answers. Again, no judgement, just an honest exploration of yourself.

What is the main reason for wanting to make this change in my life?

____

What factors, both internal and external, are creating the need for this change?

What is(are) the consequence(s) if I DO make the change?

____

____

____

____

____

____

____

____.

What is(are) the consequence(s) if I DO NOT make the change?

____

____

____

____

____

____

____

____.

Being Ready for Change

> *Once you acknowledge that change is not easy,*
> *but it is what you want to do, you are halfway there!*
> Dr. Tiza Pyle

Believing that you can change is the first step in this model, and you have worked on the first three (3) elements: a winning mindset, creating a clear picture of your desired new state, a compelling reason to do so. Now you are ready to explore one of the most challenging aspects of your journey: are you really ready to move ahead in your change?

The *Readiness for Change* concept was introduced in 1984 by James O. Prochaska and his colleagues from the University of Rhode Island.[1]

This model has been used in many change situations, particularly those that involve behavior changes and addictions. Prochaska's theory describes predictable stages that help you move along in the process, and supports you as you develop your strategies for each stage in order to move forward.

By understanding that these stages are part of change you learn not to be too hard on yourself, and to accept that your reactions to change are normal, and even predictable. Knowing this, and being open to seeking support, can accelerate your ability to move ahead in the process.

Keeping the above thought in mind, look at the *Readiness for Change* model and begin to think where you are in this process for whatever change you want to make in your life.

Pre-contemplation: Not Ready. Not considering any change. At this stage there is no plan to take any action, and people can be unaware that their present behavior creates problems. However, others observe the need for change, or may disapprove of the status quo. This person embraces the phrase, "Ignorance is bliss."

---

[1] Prochaska, J. O.; DiClemente, C. C. The transtheoretical approach: crossing traditional boundaries of therapy. Homewood, IL: Dow Jones-Irwin; 1984).

Contemplation: Getting Ready. Beginning to recognize that the behavior in question can be a problem. Ambivalent about any need for change. Weighing the pros and cons of any action that may be taken. Not planning any change within the near future. This person is "Sitting on the Fence."

Preparation: Ready to get going. Starting to think seriously about change; making plans and starting to take a few steps toward modifying life patterns that are not helpful or healthy. This person is "Testing the Waters."

Action: Doing It! Putting decisions into clear action; active participation in the process. Acquiring and putting into practice new and healthier behaviors. This person is "In the Driver's Seat."

Maintenance: Sustained change. New behavior replaces old ones. Continued commitment to sustain new behavior. In this model, this stage is also transitional, and people need to work towards preventing regressing into old habits. This person is "Cruising Along Happily."

Termination: Success – never going back. Having developed new ways of coping and not returning to old habits. Usually most people prefer to stay in **the maintenance mode**. Thus, this step is sometimes not included in the stages of change process, as it is very hard to achieve.

Another important phase that has been added to the original model by researchers and practitioners is:

Relapse: These people are "Falling off the Wagon."

This is not seen as a stage in itself, but as a return from **Action** or **Maintenance** to an earlier stage. The person can fall back into old patterns of behavior. When this happens, permanent changes in behaviors were not sustained.

It is also important to realize that this is not a linear model, and a person can go through the stages many times. Some do not experience **Relapse**. You can stay in the sustained change stage, where new habits are now part of your reality. However, for each new desired change, you may go through the phases of readiness for change, more than once or twice.

There is considerable value that can be gained from **Relapse.** This can happen, and if you accept its value, this stage can provide the opportunity to evaluate key triggers and to develop stronger strategies to sustain the desired behavioral changes.

Each time a person progresses through these various stages of change and learns from each of them, relapses then become less frequent. Also, the relapses have a shorter duration, allowing you to establish these new habits and behaviors that will sustain your desired new reality.

Having an understanding of these various stages of readiness for change can be helpful in preparing you to embark on your personal journey. In the workbook you will find questions to help you determine how prepared you are to make changes in your life. This can be a very useful step if you are thinking about a change you have attempted in the past without much success. A good example is reaching your healthy weight. Are you really ready for all the changes involved in this process? It is okay if you need more time and perhaps more preparation to make any significant change. However, you can start with small steps that will lead you to your desired future.

As you work through this, take your time answering the questions and see where you are in the cycle of readiness. Again, there are no right or wrong answers, but the opportunity to evaluate where you really are. Being ready is the magic ingredient for your success.

You will learn from Libby's story, which follows, how this model can be observed in a real-life situation. She has agreed to share her story of a difficult change she underwent when dealing with alcohol dependency. You may recognize the various phases of the readiness model as you read about her experience. It is possible that you may identify some of these in your own journey of transformation.

It is important to note that Libby's recovery from addiction is not typical. It is a success story, but many have a much harder time in reaching these results. However, significant change is possible, with a compelling reason for change, help and a plan.

Libby's Story – An illustration of readiness for change.

Libby is in her 50s; she has a demanding career, an active social life and a stable, long-term marriage. She is a very engaging and interesting woman, and her many social obligations gave her ample opportunity for "social drinking." Libby has opted for gastric bypass surgery to deal with her obesity and regain her health. She was alerted of the changes in the way she would absorb alcohol in her system after the surgery. However, she continued to drink after surgery, not only at parties, but also regularly at home.

"I did not pay much attention to this issue of alcohol absorption in my system, and believed I could handle my drinking," she said. "I have always enjoyed drinking wine, and I can handle myself."

And a couple of glasses of red wine became a bottle – night after night. And still Libby was not able to see or hear any alarm bells with this behavior.

For her, the first sign of real trouble started when she could not remember conversations she had with people, especially at night, after drinking wine.

"My friends would comment on conversations we had on the phone, or agreements I had made on these calls, and I had no idea I had talked with them. This started to worry me, and it was the first time I started to think about having to do something about my drinking."

Libby started to acknowledge that she had a real problem and started thinking seriously about solving it. This was a difficult period for her: wanting to do something, but not quite sure of what would be involved in the change. She even talked with her primary care physician who dismissed her concerns and reassured her that red wine was okay to drink, and she did not have to worry. The advice was: "take it easy" and "limit the drinking to one glass occasionally. As Libby relates: *"good advice, if you can stop at only a couple of glasses each time!"* So, her drinking continued, mostly at home, and very privately.

After a few falls in her home at night, some blackouts and more worries about the amount of wine she was drinking, Libby started reading about the signs of alcoholism, and recognized many of the symptoms in her behavior. She began to take her problem seriously and realized that she was an alcoholic and needed real help. The way she found to deal with her issues was to find a therapist specializing in addictive behavior and name her problem.

"I was surprised by two things when I told people about my decision to stop drinking alcohol," Libby told me. "The first was that, for most people, this was a non-event! They really did not care. And the people closer to me were happy that I had made this decision and were committed to helping me stay sober. My drinking had not gone as unnoticed as I had thought!"

Libby started her journey of transformation in 2015 and she continues to be sober, living in her new desired reality.

Checking Your Readiness for Change

In the following pages you will find questions that can help you analyze where you are in the various stages of this model. Use these questions as they make sense to you. Select the stages that are most meaningful to you at this time, and as a way to reinforce your desire for a new reality.

Each page is structured the same way: a short explanation of the stage and what it means, and some reflection questions. Take your time answering these, as your open answers will give you the best insight on how to reach success.

Pre-contemplation: Not Ready.

Usually, you are not thinking seriously about needing to change any current behaviors. This is common in any change process and your responses to these questions are not judgmental, but just data collection for your journey of change.

Contemplate the following:

What aspect of my life does not feel "quite right" at this moment?

____

____

____

____

____

What have I heard from family and friends about aspects of my life that could benefit from some change?

____

____

____

____

____

____.

What excuses am I making to avoid making any changes in my current life?

____

____

____

____

____

____

____.

Contemplation: Getting Ready.

Usually at this stage you start considering the possibility of real change, but are not quite ready to fully commit to the process and take concrete steps to change.

Contemplate the following:

What aspect of my life is currently creating most issues for me and what do I need to change in order to reach my goals?

____

____

____

____

____

____.

How would this change benefit me and people close to me?

____

____

____

____

____

What has prevented me from taking any action to solve this issue?

____

____

____

____

____

____

____

____.

Preparation: I'm Ready

Usually this stage is the start of the journey. You start taking small steps, accept the negative consequences of the status quo, and believing change is necessary and beneficial for you.

Contemplate the following:

Now that I have identified what I want to change, how can I create a plan for this change?

____

____

____

____

____

____.

What resources are available to me to make this change a success?

____

____

____

____

____

____.

Who can best support me in this process to help me succeed?

____

____

____

____

____

____

____.

Action: I'm Doing

This stage involves concrete steps that lead to real change in behavior. You will be actively involved in the process. Some doubts may still be present, and there is a danger to stop and return to old behaviors. The ***B.A.S.E. Model for Change*** will guide you in developing a concrete and customized plan for your change.

Contemplate the following:

What are the concrete steps I have taken or need to take?

____

____

____

____

____

What help do I need to be able to sustain this plan?

____

____

____

____

____.

Some Final Thoughts on Being Ready for Change and Addictive Behaviors

In a conversation with a therapist who specializes in addictive behaviors, I learned that:

- One of the biggest barriers to recovery is the inability to move beyond the **contemplation** or **preparation phases** of the *Readiness for Change* cycle.
- It takes a lot of determination to move into **action** and stay the course.
- Understanding and accepting the process of change is a great step in the road to recovery.
- Being ashamed is not uncommon, and can delay recovery.
- Denial of a problem can greatly delay its resolution.
- Accepting that there is a problem is a key element in any change process.
- Finding help and creating a plan leads to success.

Although the *Readiness for Change* model is used in the recovery of addictive behaviors, understanding the model can help you with any type of change you want to make.

Summary of your Exploration – Belief

Record below what you have learned while doing this first step of the B.A.S.E. model:

Mindset:

____

____

____

____

____

____

____.

Vision:

____

____

____

____

____

____.

Compelling Reason:

____

____

____

____

____

____

____.

Readiness for Change:

____

____

____

____

____

____

____

____

____.

ACCEPTANCE

> *Acceptance is an act of humility, when you recognize the good, the bad and the ugly in you, and make the choice to change what you do not like.*
>
> Dr. Tiza Pyle

The second step of the model is **Acceptance** – another key element of any change process.

Until you fully acknowledge that whatever you are doing currently is not working well for you, and decide to take a different direction, real and sustainable change may not happen. This step in the model is essential and it takes hard work!

As with the first step, this one also has 3 basic components listed below:

- **Self-awareness**: knowing and accepting who you really are.
- **Letting go of the past**: deciding to let go in order to move forward.
- **Accepting the "in between space:"** living with uncertainty, where a desired state is not fully realized, and the past no longer works well.

Each step is explained in more detail in the following pages. There are suggested questions and exercises to help you continue to gather information for the successful completion of your desired change.

Self-Awareness

You are a unique person, and your response to change will be just as unique. Sometimes others' expectations can cause unnecessary stress. This can be greatly reduced if you develop a very good idea of who you are, what is your personal response to change, and how you move forward in a way that makes the best sense to you. Once this picture is clear in your mind, it becomes easier to articulate to others what you need and how to develop a plan that meets your goals and preferences. If you have taken any personality or preference assessments use this information to support you in the change process.

The questions below give you an opportunity to start your self-discovery journey.

How do I respond to changes in my life?

____

____

____

____

____.

Looking at my experiences to date, when have I been successful in making a significant change in my life?

____

____

____

____

____

____.

What helped in my success?

Given the change I'm considering, or have made, what are two or three habits I need to change in order to be successful in reaching my desired new life?

What must I do differently to change the above habits?

What impact might the change I'm contemplating, or have already made, have in my life?

What impact might the change I'm contemplating, or have made, have on the lives of others who matter to me?

____

____

____

____

____

____

____

____

____.

What might be the consequences, positive or negative, if I do not make these necessary changes?

____

____

____

____

____

____

____

____.

Who might be negatively impacted, and how, by the changes I'm making or have made?

____

____

____

____

____

____.

Self-awareness takes courage, and knowing yourself and fully accepting who you are, can be important steps towards your success in life. Following is Mark's account of his journey and how accepting who he really is made a significant difference in reaching his goals. You can do the same!

Mark is a very intelligent and motivated marketing executive who was struggling in his current position and was looking for support moving forward. He agreed to share his journey of growth, and the positive outcome of increased self-awareness. Accepting who he really is made a significant difference in reaching his goals. In his case, concrete evidence of positive changes happened when he started receiving encouraging feedback from key people in his professional life. And, he continues to experience positive outcomes resulting from these behavioral changes.

Mark recognizes that his journey is never-ending and will continue to strive to work towards more constructive behaviors, including coaching and developing others and creating effective teams as a way to solidify his skills as a leader. He is now aware when his behaviors are not as constructive as he would like and will not lead to the results he desires.

As a result of these important changes and his acquired self-awareness, Mark has been recruited for and accepted a new position as Director of Marketing in a different organization. He has experienced success in his new role and continues to be aware of the need to attend to both the task and the needs of the people on his team.

This personal account of a journey of change is a great testimonial of the importance of self-awareness as a key element of long term, sustainable change.

Change is possible, and it takes work and commitment. You can do the same!

Mark's Story: The power of self-awareness for change.

As an undergraduate, I studied Engineering, but quickly realized that marketing was my passion. A year after finishing my undergraduate degree, I applied for and entered business school to pursue a career in marketing. My first job was at a leading Consumer Package Goods company. Like many, I started my career with a 'class' of marketers hungry to get ahead in the industry.

I excelled early in my career and immediately felt I was on the fast track to becoming Director or VP, running a team of innovative marketers.

However, after changing organizations and not finding my footing in two subsequent jobs, I eventually realized not only was I no longer on the fast track to Senior Leadership, I had fallen behind my peers. I was permanently stalled at the Manager level.

After another rough start at the fourth job, and after using an assessment tool offered by my organization, ***I finally realized it was not others holding me back, it was me.***

I was raised by loving parents who were each one of the first to graduate from college in their families. They instilled the classic message that if you work hard, opportunities like career advancement will be the result. They were not able to educate me about the other essential element of success at work: understanding the culture of organizations and the ability to form alliances. I valued getting things done well, ***but I did not value building relationships****. I had not created those important alliances to help me get to where I wanted to be in my career*

Here was my challenge: ***After years of operating one way, can I change how I view work situations and learn new ways to interact at work while maintaining my values and integrity?***

I learned in this past year of hard work that ***you can!*** *And I'm on my way to make these important changes in my life.*

After reflection, and with the help of a coach, I became aware that my personal style was holding me back from being the leader I wanted to be. It took me a while to see some of my thought patterns and behaviors for what they were, a barrier to my success.

My plan for change, with the support of coaching, was to do the following:

- *Develop a more effective leadership style*
- *Explore new ways of working to get the best out of others and myself*
- *Build my brand within my organization as a strong leader*
- *Build advocates at the Executive level for career progression*

I was able to identify behaviors that needed to change so I could achieve my goals. During the coaching meetings we discussed what underlying feelings, emotions, triggers and assumptions lead to those behaviors I wanted to modify. We also identified tangible changes in thoughts, actions, and words that would better reinforce the changes I was making, and also drive changes in the perception of how co-workers, agency partners, and leadership viewed my leadership skills.

Letting Go of the Past

The past is an integral part of who you are. But it cannot become an anchor that holds you back. You must let go if you want to move forward. Until you tackle this "letting go" process, there is a danger of allowing the past to hold you back – preventing you from reaching your goals and the future you want.

As you prepare to move into your new reality, there is a belief as you move forward your past must be denied. This is untrue, and it is essential to realize the value of your past in the process of change.

Personal transformation asks you to understand and respect who you are and what you have done, without assigning blame or "right and wrong" for your present or past reality. Every change requires letting go of something, and sometimes includes a mourning period over what is about to end – because you are giving up something that is familiar. Hanging on to a past you want to change delays your journey and robs you of the energy needed for your transformation.

This is the time when you must leave the old reality behind and contemplate a future not yet fully known or defined. Endings involve a process of identifying what you believe needs to end, and most importantly "letting go" of the behaviors, thoughts, etc. that are no longer helpful to you. Also, you will need to recognize that past is no longer a viable reality. This does not mean that you ignore or forget previous alliances, accomplishments and values. These are to be remembered, honored and even mourned! But if you really want to move ahead, the past must lose its hold.

Below are some questions to check your readiness to let go of the past:

What do I need to honor and hold onto about my past that can help me in the future?

____

____

____

____.

What do I need to let go of to move forward?

What support do I need to seek out in order to move beyond my current reality?

Following is Sandra's story. She offers a good example of how learning to "let go of the past" allowed her to create a new life for herself and her family.

In her process of personal transformation, Sandra is learning how to modify old behaviors and create experiences that can support her new life, and the choices she has made.

The next phase in the process involves recognizing the value and learning from the discomfort and uncertainties of the "in between" stage of your transition. This is an integral part of creating your new life. There are great opportunities and new challenges when you have the power to shape your future!

Sandra's Story – Letting go and living a new reality

When she was diagnosed with unspecified Crohn's disease, complicated by serious obesity, Sandra realized that much needed to change. A way to deal with her illness was surgery which would result in considerable weight loss, and she needed to be prepared to face this significant change in her life.

> "*A massive change was our socialization, and how we got together with friends and family. My friends know I don't eat out anymore because it challenges my willpower. I'm in the restaurant business, so going out was very much part of our family routine. The same holds true for my "kitchen experiments" as a chef, and wanting to prepare these elaborate meals every time family and friends would come over. My life revolved around food, and I needed to make significant changes to shift the focus from just food and being in the kitchen.*
>
> *It is sad that we don't entertain nearly as much as we did. But the behavior modification is reinforced every time I look in the mirror, or revel in how delighted my family is with the "new me." And, that's what counts most."*
>
> "*One very interesting change is that I'm finally learning to enjoy the company of family and friends. My kitchen used to be my retreat. And my role in both our families was to be this "experimental scientist" concocting new dishes while the rest socialized in other rooms. Today, I'm not in the kitchen nearly as much as I used to be. I'm a part of the conversation, I'm learning more about these people, their likes and dislikes. And it's fun.*
>
> *I'm still growing comfortable with this profound change in how I relate to others. But in doing so, and gauging the results so far, I understand why you have to give up familiar habits if you want to realize new – and better – dividends in life."*

Accepting and Living in the "In-Between Space"

This "in-between" space is a great opportunity to recognize your personal needs and then act on them. Taking steps to identify where actions are centered in need and not guilt, seems harder for women than men. But it's something you must do for your own self-improvement. Social pressures and expectations tend to place women in roles of subservience, which makes it easier to forget that we must serve ourselves first – before we can conscientiously serve others.

Following are some questions you can ask yourself to support you in this "in between" space of your personal transformational journey:

How do I personally respond to uncertainty in my life? Think about some concrete examples of how you react dealing with the unknown.

____

____

____

____

____.

What are the most important elements I need/want to have in a meaningful future?

____

____

____

____

____.

What additional information do I need to gather in order to become more comfortable with the change I want to make?

____

____

____

____

____

____

____

____.

How do I ensure I can get all the information I need to become more comfortable with my desired change?

____

____

____

____

____

____

____

____.

Summary of your Exploration – Acceptance

Use the space below to create a summary of what you have learned about in this second step of the ***B.A.S.E Model for Change***.

Self-awareness: Knowing and accepting who you really are.

____

____

____

____

____

____

Letting go of the past: Deciding to let go in order to move forward.

____

____

____

____

____

____

____

____.

Accepting the "in between space:" Living with uncertainty, where a desired state is not fully realized, and the past no longer works well.

SUPPORT

Asking for help is not easy for most people. Since an important part of the model is to help you learn the value of seeking and finding support, I think that we all need to learn how to do this effectively. When we ask others for support, we are giving them the opportunity to be contributors to our success. This is a gift!

I really like the thought: *"You have to do it (the change)* ***yourself****, but it does not have to be* ***by yourself*****!"**

Below are some of the components of seeking support:

- Clarity of your goals: knowing what I need and how others can help.
- Letting go of control: understanding that asking for help is not a weakness.
- Where to find help: the tactical aspect of support.

Asking for help is not an easy task. It is very common in our culture to think that you are expected to do it all – especially if you are a woman! In this journey of transformation spend some time exploring this topic and you will be surprised to find that asking for help can be a real gift to others, who are ready and willing to lend you support.

One type of support that can be of great value to you is to identify somebody who could become your accountability partner, who would help you stay on track. Take the time to identify those people in your life that can be your partners in this journey.

To help you find the best type of support you need, the questions below can be a good start.

Clarity of Goals

Which of the steps I have identified as part of my overall goal can be delegated to others?

____.

How can I best communicate my desired outcome to others, so they know what help I need?

____.

How could I use the support of others to further identify opportunities for further delegation?

Letting Go of Control

Identify the situations when it was difficult for me to let others help.

____

____

____

____

____

____

____

____.

List benefits for me to get help.

____

____

____

____

____

____

____

____.

What do I need to do in order to allow others to help me?

____

____

____

____

____

____

____

____

____.

Where to Find Help

Who among my network has offered to help me?

____

____

____

____

____

____

____

____

____.

What skills are needed to help me achieve my goals and who among my network has these?

____

____

____

____

____

____

____

____.

What resources do I have in my community/work to find the type of help I need?

Summary of your Exploration – Support

Below is some space for you to create the summary of what you have learned from your exploration of this Step Three in the ***B.A.S.E. Model for Change***.

Clarity of your goals: Knowing what I need and how others can help.

____

____

____

____

____

____

____.

Letting go of control: Understanding that asking for help is not a weakness.

____

____

____

____

____

____

____.

Where to find help: The tactical aspect of support.

____

____

____

____

____

____

____

____

____.

EXECUTION

A great idea remains only a dream, unless you can create a real plan to bring the dream to reality. Sometimes this step is ignored, and results are not achieved. This step is the HOW section of the process. A personal plan will help you to reach your goals.

At this stage of your journey of change, you need to –

- Commit to a plan
- Review your priorities
- Examine your time management preferences

Below are questions to help you identify how to best start the Fourth Step, which is the Execution phase of your personal transformation. Your goal is to find two or three key answers to each question. Take your time. Be honest with yourself. This is for you only. They will help you develop a picture of what you need to do in order to develop a meaningful plan for lasting change.

Based on my experience, what is the best way to create a plan to get things done?

____

____

____

____

____

____

____

____.

What have I identified as my key priorities?

How are my current activities supporting what I really want to accomplish?

What concrete steps do I need to take to achieve my current goals?

What will I need in order to create the necessary time to achieve my goals?

Please note: Making a clear plan for change does not have to be complicated. The key elements of the plan are:

- Reasons for your change
- Benefits to you and to others (family, co-workers, community, etc.)
- Detailed plan with ways to measure success
- Clear steps
- Completion dates
- Celebration of your success

On the following pages you will find some examples of plans for four (4) different situations:

- Reaching your healthy weight
- Finding a job
- Changing a behavior
- Moving to a new city

These are only samples to give you an idea of how a plan for change can look. Yours may be very different and the important part is to make sure you include enough detail to make the plan a real road map for your success. Again, there is no right or wrong. This is a tool to help you track your progress.

Much of the information summarized in the plan is not new to you, as you have identified these in the earlier steps of the ***B.A.S.E. Model for Change***.

And, as mentioned in the plan, make sure your plan is very personal and meets your needs to complete the change successfully. Dates and deadlines are important and these need to be realistic and doable. Commit only to a timetable that is right for you.

Additional suggestions:

- Keep the plan visible and modify as needed.
- Keep your end result present. Realize the road may have bumps and detours, but you can get to where you want to be.
- Keep your compelling reason in mind; revisit it when needed and keep going.

You can do it!

Healthy Weight Plan
SAMPLE

This is only a sample to give you an idea of how a plan for change can look. Yours may be very different. Make sure your plan is very personal and meets your needs, and challenges you to complete the change successfully.

Type of Change: Reach my healthy weight

Reason for your change:

- I want to be able to participate in outdoor activities that require walking and hiking in the national parks with my family. I'm tired of being on the sidelines because of my unhealthy weight.
- I want to regain my health and become more active.

Benefits:

For me: Increase stamina, ability to do what I like to do, give me the ability to exercise regularly without pain, participate in activities with family and friends, reduce sense of "self-pity," get new clothes, improve self-confidence.

For my family: Be able to plan outdoors activities, less stress in family outings, and be a healthier person in their lives long term.

Plan:

- Over the next 10 weeks I will modify my eating and activities to allow me to lose at least 1 lb. per week. This will start on (date) ___________________.
- By (date) __________ I will reach my initial goal of ______________ lbs. I can repeat this process until I reach my healthy weight of _____________.

I will measure progress by:

- Weekly weigh ins
- Daily food journal

Steps for Food and Activity

- Plan my food intake – 3 meals/day without snacks
- Stop eating grains, with the exception of oatmeal
- Increase number of vegetable servings daily
- Track what I eat—no "good or bad" attached. Only collecting data
- Find a tracking app I can commit to use
- Walk for 3o minutes 3x/week (enter days and times)
- Join an exercise class (in a gym or online) 3x /week – (Enter location, dates and times)
- Track my weight once/week on Saturday
- Reward myself when I lose at least 4 lbs./month (clothing or accessories, movie, jewelry, etc.)

KEEP THIS PLAN VISIBLE AND MAKE CHANGES AS NEEDED.
YOU CAN DO IT

Moving to a New Location
SAMPLE

This is only a sample to give you an idea of how a plan for change can look. Yours may be very different. Make sure your plan is very personal and meets your needs, and challenges you to complete the change successfully.

Type of Change: Selling my home and changing to a new location near family.

Reasons for your change:

- Since I lost my husband, living in my current large house has become too much for me. In addition, my children are not near, and I would prefer to be close to them and the grandchildren.

- I understand this is not going to be an easy change as I'm leaving a community I know, friends and memories.

Benefits:

For me: Have more support from my children and grandchildren. Move to a larger city with more opportunities to participate in cultural events I enjoy. Better climate and milder winters. Less work in maintaining a large house.

For my family: Less worry about having me alone and far away.

Plan:

- Decide on type of house that will best fit my needs.
- Working with family (if relevant) to identify best location for a new house search.
- Make a list of "must have" and "like to have" to help define my house search.
- Select realtor in the new location to start house search.
- Select realtor in my current location to start house selling process.

I will measure progress by:

- The number of tasks I complete each week towards getting ready to sell my current house.
- The number of houses I see in the new location that meet my criteria.
- The number of showings and offers for my current house.

Steps in the process:

To sell my house. I will:

- By (date) start going room by room and deciding what I want to move and what I will sell/donate/throw away.
- Decide what I will do myself and what will require other's help.
- Identify who can help me in this process.
- Determine a budget for move.
- Work with the realtor to make a plan to put the house on the market.
- Set a date to complete all preparations and place the house on the market.

To buy my new house, I will:

- By (date) visit the new city and select a realtor.
- Work with local realtor to identify properties that meet my criteria.
- Set a time (date) to spend 2 or 3 days in new location to see houses.
- Decide on a target date to have this done.
- Identify financial resources needed.

Ways to Celebrate Progress, I will:

- Buy flowers.
- Reward myself with something I really like.
- Go to a movie/theatre.
- Find other enjoyable "treats." ___________

Note: the actual move may require a new change plan!!

KEEP YOUR PLAN VISIBLE AND MAKE CHANGES AS NEEDED.
YOU CAN DO IT

Changing a Behavior
SAMPLE

This is only a sample to give you an idea of how a plan for change can look. Yours may be very different. Make sure your plan is very personal, and meets your needs and challenges you to complete the change successfully.

Type of Change: Becoming a better listener

Reasons for your change:

Through feedback from family and work colleagues, I have realized that I do not listen to others and as a result I miss important information. In addition, I'm being perceived as uncaring and self-centered.

My reason to make this change is to develop an important skill that can better support my career aspirations and to improve communication with others both at home and at work.

Benefits:

For me: I will create a more positive perception of my communication ability and my intensions when interfacing with others. Improve my ability to get the whole picture of a problem.

For others at home and at work: I will be able to make better decisions based on the whole picture and all the facts, rather than assumptions based on partial information. I will show interest and respect for others' ideas and learn from them.

Plan:

When others come to talk with me, I will:

- Stop what I'm doing and be fully present in the conversation.

- Acknowledge that the person needs to talk with me, but now may not be the best time, so I will set up a time very soon to do this.
- Not interrupt the person while they are talking, and pay full attention to what is being said, rather than be thinking about an answer.

I will measure progress by:

- Noting when I do not interrupt others during a conversation.
- Practicing being present in the moment to pay attention to others.
- Being aware of the many times I have made assumptions without hearing all the facts.

Steps to improve my listening skills:

- Starting now, during meetings at work I will make sure I do not interrupt others. I will make quick notes of my thoughts on the subject and bring these up when appropriate.
- I will share with colleagues my desire to improve listening skills and ask for feedback if I'm not listening to them.
- By (date) I will complete a learning program dealing with listening skills. I will research availability of programs in my organization or online.
- I will start practicing asking better, open ended questions to make sure I get the whole picture.
- I'm committed to practice new behaviors and make this change.

Ways to Celebrate Progress:

- I will share my progress with a trusted friend.
- After reaching one of my goals, I will reward myself with something I really like.
- When I receive positive feedback from others, I will stop and recognize the progress I have made.
- Other ___________

KEEP YOUR PLAN VISIBLE AND MAKE CHANGES AS NEEDED.
YOU CAN DO IT

Finding a New Job
SAMPLE

This is only a sample to give you an idea of how a plan for change can look. Yours may be very different. Make sure your plan is very personal, and meets your needs and challenges you to complete the change successfully.

Type of Change: To find a job that better fits my long-term objectives and skills

Reasons for your change:

- My organization has gone through a series of re-organizations and my current job has changed and no longer uses my best skills.

- I want to find a new position in an organization that has a culture that better fits my values and better utilizes my skills in customer service.

- I want to make a salary that allows me to have a comfortable life and be able to save for retirement.

Benefits:

For me: Less stress, higher motivation to go to work, increased sense of purpose in my job, compensation that meets my needs.

For my family: I will have more energy to participate in family activities and be more available to all working for an organization that values life-work balance. Better salary will permit me to save for extras that can benefit all.

Plan:

- Starting this coming week, I will start planning my job search strategy.

- By _____ (date) I will have revised my resume and gotten feedback from two (2) people who I trust and have the skills to help me on this (Name the people you can use.)

- Starting on ______ (date) I will research open positions in my field and desired job title.
- By ______(date) I will have identified at least five (5) organizations that have the culture I'm looking for.

- Starting this coming week, I will make a list of people I can interview about best strategies to organize a job search.

- I will explore the possibility of hiring a career coach to support me in this process.

- By _______(date) I will start applying for key open positions.

- By _______(date) I would like to have at least one job offer (understand that it takes time to find a new job and allow the needed time to find the best fit.)

I will measure progress by:

- The number of networking contact I make each week.
- The number of applications I complete.
- The number of call backs and the number of interviews for a new job.

Steps for a Successful Job search:

- Update your resume and get feedback on the final product.
- Tailor your resume to your profession/desired job.
- Learn about current recruiting practices used by employers. These have changed considerably in the last couple of years.
- Identify the key words for your job search. Use these when searching for open positions.
- Research key job boards used by the industry you are targeting.
- Register on these boards to ensure you are informed of openings that fit your search criteria.
- Plan to apply for jobs that fit your criteria.
- Develop a tracking system to follow up on your applications.
- Identify people you might know in your desired new organization.

- At some point let your current manager know you are interested in a new position, because this information can become known to your employer in an active job search.
- If you are looking for a job and are no longer employed, be prepared to tell prospective employers why you are available in the job market.
- Since most coaches offer complimentary sessions to determine best fit, research available coaches in this area to help you in this process.
- Develop a realistic date by when you expect to have a new position. Make it happen!

Ways to Celebrate Progress:

- buying flowers
- enjoying something I really like to do
- going to a movie/theatre
- Other ___________

KEEP YOUR PLAN VISIBLE AND MAKE CHANGES AS NEEDED.
YOU CAN DO IT!

Action Plan for Change

Following is a template that you can use to develop your own personal plan for change.

A. Desired Change and Compelling Reason	
List below: The change you want to make (use some detail to help you with the plan) The main reason for this change (what will give you motivation to change)	
B. Benefits	
To me (list at least 3 benefits)	To others (Team/Organization/Family)

C. Barriers and Strategies for Success

Barriers: what can hold me back	Strategy: how can I overcome these

D. Action Steps

Action (List concrete actions/steps you can take, with measurements)

Note: Use additional pages if needed for a complete plan.

E. Involvement of Others (If appropriate)	
Action Person 1 2. 3.	How/What

F. Showing Progress	
Action 1. 2. 3	Measurement of Progress/Success 1. 2. 3.

Summary of your Exploration – Execution

Below is space to record what you have identified as steps in the last step of the model: Getting it Done.

Plan I have developed to reach my goal

____

____

____

____

____

____

____

Key priorities

____

____

____

____

____

____

Time management preferences

____

____

____

____

____

____

____

____

____

____.

Chapter 3 – Stages of Transition

> *"Just when the caterpillar thought the world was ending, she turned into a butterfly."*
>
> — Proverb

Transition is an internal process that happens within people during times of change. It is an integral part of any personal transformation.

Dr. William Bridges published his book *Transitions: Making Sense of Life's Changes.*[2]. and introduced the concept of the powerful internal psychological process of change. It was a work that revolutionized the understanding of what happens to people during those times of external pressures and upheaval. As he explains, change happens externally. It is something you can observe and is usually perceived by others as well. But when people are faced with almost any type of change, there is another hidden internal process that must take place. It is a journey you must take in order to navigate the external pressures and reach, with some degree of success, this new reality that you need to both understand and accept. And this happens not only when change is imposed upon us, but also when we initiate change ourselves. This is the micro – very personal – side of the change process.

Transition – the people side of change – is defined as ***the psychological process that takes place at the individual level when external changes are present.***

---

[2] Bridges, William. *Transitions: Making Sense of Life's Changes,* 2nd edition. Da Capo Press, Cambridge, MA, 2004

And this internal journey of change and transformation has predictable stages, that are normal and expected checkpoints to ensure you are on your way:

- Endings: Losses and letting go of the past.
- Living in the In-Between Space: Dealing with uncertainty or ambiguity, and the unknown.
- New Beginnings: Having a clear vision of your desired future; moving towards a new reality.

Just to remind you, endings are the start of the process, but in real life experiences, the new beginnings are thrusted upon you, and you will need to deal with that, before you have time to address the endings piece. Or, the in-between stages could have already started. Your known reality is gone, and you are not quite in a comfortable place in the new beginning. Each of the stages in the transition process is important and they need to be addressed at some time. This will help you organize your thoughts and better navigate the changes you are experiencing while making better sense of them. Also, you will be able to deal in a more effective way with the external change.

First Phase: Endings – Letting Go of the Past

> *"When one life ends, another begins."*
> Buddha

The first phase of transition involves the necessary "Endings" – what you must leave behind.

When change happens, either by your choice or imposed by circumstances outside your control, a new reality is created. And you must enter unfamiliar territory, something you do not know or have not yet experienced. Your present may be painful. But it is known. And there is a strong measure of comfort in familiarity. But growth requires some change, and you will need to take the risk of letting go of what you know, your past.

In the second step of the ***B.A.S.E. Model for Change*** you have explored letting go of your past. Here is some additional information on this important step.

Fear of the unknown is not a weakness, but something that has been hardwired in our brains as a way to keep us safe. So, letting go of the past you know can be challenging, but is a necessary step of self-development and growth.

Change also involves the need to mourn your past. This is not surprising, as you will be dealing with the loss of what you know. The process of grief is healthy and allows you to explore your feelings and emotions about your change and be free to move forward. Grief is present in any change, and you will find information on the stages of grief in Additional Resources in this workbook.

As you embark on your journey, take time to explore how your life and experiences have helped you. This can provide you with helpful insights on how your entire system of living may need change. This exploration can also include looking at long-ago learned behaviors, beliefs, habits and even relationships that are now part of your life, which might deserve serious review.

Do not be afraid to "be afraid." Fear can be healthy because it makes us able to consider options and consequences. No change is easy. And though you are not fearless, you can control your fears. The decision to reshape your life – and yourself – has both risks and rewards. Believing in yourself and the possibilities that lie ahead of you will provide the strength you need to move into your desired future.

This is the time when you must leave the old reality behind and contemplate a future not yet fully known or defined. Endings involve a process of identifying losses and most importantly "letting go" of what no longer serves you well. To really move ahead, your past must be honored, but not hold you back.

Second Phase: The "In-Between-Space"

> *"Go confidently in the direction of your dreams,*
> *live the life you imagined."*
> Henry David Thoreau

The second stage of transition is the "In-Between" stage.

Perhaps the most challenging time in any personal transformation is learning how to accept and be comfortable in the difficult "in-between" spaces of your metamorphosis: when all the changes start to happen.

You're not the person you were, but not yet who you want to be and what you want to do. This is an integral stage of all personal change with much confusion and uncertainty. But it is also exciting, once you understand how to best take advantage of new possibilities.

This is the time when you will need to live with the ambiguity of not quite knowing the future and realizing the past must be gone. This is a phase of great opportunity for innovation and new thinking. Embracing this complex stage is important and can lead to the creation of your exciting new reality.

You can create your future, and be who you really want to be, doing what you want to do. But it takes time, effort, and a commitment to move – sometimes relentlessly and not always swiftly – through this phase of your transition.

This "in-between" space is a great opportunity to recognize your personal needs and then act on them. Taking steps to identify where actions are centered (in need, not guilt) seems harder for women than men. But it's something you must do for your own self-improvement. Social pressures and expectations tend to place women in roles of subservience, which makes it easier to forget that we must serve ourselves first – before we can conscientiously serve others.

The ***B.A.S.E Model for Change*** deals with these two stages of the transitions process in the **Awareness** step and you have identified the key aspects you need to let go in order to move forward.

Third Phase: New Beginnings: Your Desired Future

The final phase of the process is "New Beginnings" – when you have created a picture of your new desired future. The new reality is now the present. In this stage, planning and strategies are fully implemented, and the individual – or the organization – is living in a new reality and benefitting from the changes. You have created a clear picture of your desired future earlier. Below are some further thoughts that can support you in some types of changes, such as changing jobs, or moving into a new community.

How can I ensure that I have the skills and knowledge needed in this new reality?

____

____

____

____

____

____

____.

What new behaviors or habits do I need to sustain the changes?

____

____

____

____

____

____.

What support do I need for my success in this new reality?

____

____

____

____

____

____

____

____

____.

By understanding these basic principles of the "people side of change," it will become easier for you to be better prepared to move ahead and redefine your reality – and create a more exciting future for yourself!

Final Thoughts

Completing this workbook has been a journey and hopefully you benefitted from the exploration and reflection.

Congratulations for taking concrete steps to achieve your dreams and aspirations.

In the end, when creating a new lifestyle that supports your goals, all stand to benefit. That's not to say these changes won't create tension among family and friends along the way, or at least puzzle them. This is why you must work to make others understand – even if only by your actions – that there's something in it for them, too. Some might even make you feel guilty of your "misplaced" agenda. So be careful not to slip back into old habits of, "Oh, my children or my spouse need me more." And don't confuse misplaced guilt for need, especially if you're being quietly pressured into *not* doing what is important to you by those who know how to push your "guilt buttons." Keep strong and focused. Both are vital in modifying your new thoughts and habits.

The importance of learning how to attend to your own needs was made very clear to me during one of my many air travels. When I *really* heard what the flight attendant was saying: ***"Put your mask on first before helping others."*** It was clear that self-care is not a selfish act. Self-preservation is essential to successfully reaching our life's purpose, even when that purpose is service to others.

You may need to learn how to be clear about what you need and want. When one's reality starts to change, others can strive to keep the "status quo," which ends up being at your spiritual expense. As you learn to recognize how relationships are impacted by your transformation, you'll likely learn to better deal with such potential "distractions of spirit," and discover how to stay your course.

Learning to develop new habits and routines for a different reality you want are the major challenges experienced during transitional periods that we all must go through. And this series of experiences helps us to understand how the changes we've undergone become catalysts for new roles – and a lifestyle you may not have experienced before. Embrace this growth as a gift and use it to your advantage.

All true change takes effort and commitment. Personal transformations are very rewarding and hard to achieve without strong resolve. Motivation is something that only you can find. But once it is found, that inspiration is a key element in your success.

How to Engage with Dr. Tiza

My principal reason for writing this workbook is to share with others who want to make changes in their lives, that which I have learned from my experience and my own journey of transformation. This journey is described in my book: *Fat Hurts: Your Guide to Transformation After Weight Loss Surgery*, 2016, where I described the process offered to you in this workbook. This early work is available at Amazon.com.

I welcome your comments, suggestions and ideas on the topics of personal transformation and change. We can learn from each other to achieve our goals.

Visit our website YourPathToSuccessCoaching.com and you can leave messages and comments on the site. Use the ***Contact Us*** area to communicate with us.

Resources are also available on the site in the tab named **Book Resources.** You will find templates and tools to help you in your journey.

You can also reach me via e-mail, on social media, at both LinkedIn and Facebook.

E-mail: Tiza@YourPathtoSuccessCoaching.com
Facebook page: YourPathtoSuccessCoaching
LinkedIn: https://www.linkedin.com/in/tizapyle

I look forward to hearing from you.

Dr. Tiza

About the Author

Dr. Beatriz (Tiza) M. Pyle, (PhD) is a coach, consultant and author who has experienced change in her life and can bring to her work first-hand knowledge of what it means to experience and conquer the difficulties of personal change and transformation.

She is committed to guide each client to achieve results and reach their goals, using tested tools and processes that lead to personal transformation.

Her current coaching and consulting practice is focused on improving team effectiveness in organizations, through behavior changes and commitment to a goal, and working with individuals who want to make changes in their lives. Also, many of her clients, recognizing that good health is a key factor in performing at one's best, have started looking for different approaches to their personal development—those that include a more balanced outlook to their lives, including health and nutrition goals. This has reinforced Tiza's own belief in the importance of wellness in ones' life, and it is supported by her own experience. She was able to regain her health and energy in her 60's by tackling her own obesity problem and developing an exciting, more active lifestyle after significant weight loss. This was a major transformation in her own life.

Tiza's current work is rooted in the belief that "an active longevity" is a reachable goal. And she is committed to support her clients in developing a doable plan for a productive, long life.

Having completed a year-long training program in nutrition and wellness coaching at the Institute for Integrative Nutrition (IIN) in 2013, Tiza offers her clients an opportunity to work on a holistic approach to life as an integral part of their individual transformation.

Tiza's formal education includes:

- PhD in Education from Loyola University of Chicago
- Master's degree in Human Resources Management from Loyola University of Chicago
- BS degree in Education at the Universidade Federal de Minas Gerais, Brazil
- Graduate from the Institute for Integrative Nutrition (IIN) as a Health Coach

Tiza is the Founder and CEO of Pyle Consulting Group, Inc. and offers coaching programs as *Your Path to Success Coaching*, a division of Pyle Consulting Group, Inc. She and her husband live in St. Charles, Il.

Acknowledgments

Writing a book is a humbling experience. You soon realize it will take a lot longer than anticipated and that the support of many is needed. This is not my first book, and past experience helps, but there are so many steps in the process that it is challenging. I could not have completed this project without the help of many who partnered with me in this journey.

My heartfelt thanks go to all who have contributed to this workbook with your thoughtful comments and your encouragement. I want to make sure you know how much I appreciate your participation and support. My coaching clients have provided me with many valuable insights and many thanks for the lessons I have learned from you. I'm also very grateful to all who shared their stories so others can learn from your wisdom and experiences.

I am particularly grateful to Susan Nunn, my editor, who took me under her wing and kept me on track. Her intelligent and judicious input and a marvelous sense of style made this book so much better. Thank you! www.CSusanNunn.com

A very special "thank you" goes to Ariel Reis who, through her very creative illustrations, brought to life some of my ideas in a fun and engaging way. I'm truly grateful for your contribution.

Others who contributed to this process include Stephen Perrault, owner of Wellspring Creative Communications, who offered me editorial support at the start of the project. Your input is very much appreciated. Members of our monthly discussion group, Women Leaders in Business, and other colleagues read early editions of this work and provided valuable feedback. Thank you for your gift of time and thoughtful comments.

I could not have undertaken this project without the support of my dear husband, Roger, and my wonderful family and friends, who listened to me and offered encouragement to keep going – especially at those times when I questioned what I was doing. Thank you so much.

Many others also provided me with support and friendship during this process. I thank you all! Your feedback is greatly appreciated! I'm very grateful that you cared!

Resources

Title	Description
10 Golden Rules for Personal Transformation	This tool offers ideas that can accelerate your change process and help you develop habits to sustain the new reality you want to create. You can use it as a checklist of helpful hints to support your journey of change and transformation.
The Wheel of Your Life	This tool provides you with a quick way to create a snapshot of your present. It also offers an opportunity to identify those areas that are important to you, and that may need some focus and attention.
12 Habits of Happy People	Happiness is possible when you develop the skills to see life in a positive way. This tool suggests 12 ways to identify opportunities for positive thinking and creating a sense of well-being.
5 Stages of Grief	Letting go of the past involves a process of grief, and grief occurs as the result of the loss of something that matters to you. And the common factor in these events is change. This tool provides an awareness of the stages of grief to help you better understand the feelings that inevitably accompany loss.
Morning Pages	This tool offers a powerful way to move your thoughts into action. If you enjoy writing, this could be an excellent vehicle for you. It could be a fun way to open possibilities and options that may appear unavailable to you right now during this journey of transformation.

Find these individual tools in their totality on pages to follow:

10 Golden Rules for Personal Change: Developing New Habits for Success

10 Golden Rules for Personal Change offers you some ideas that can accelerate your change process and help you develop new habits to sustain the new reality you want to create.

1. **Select only one thing to change at any given time. You must be committed to that change.** Make sure that the change you want to make is important to you; and, that you are prepared to do what it takes to make it happen. You will only change if what you want to accomplish really matters to you.

2. **Develop a written plan of what you want to accomplish and how you are going to do it.** Writing down what you want to accomplish will help you reach your objective. As you put a plan on paper, this becomes a stronger reality for you. Make it simple and keep the plan visible!

3. **Develop a support network**. There will be times when you will falter – you can count on this. Developing a support network provides you with a source of encouragement, when you need it. Learn to ask for help! And add this to your written plan: Who is in your support network?

4. **Know what motivates you**. Before you start any change process, make sure that you clearly know why you are embarking on this journey and what is in it for you. Your motivation is what got you started, and you need to make sure it stays present during the process.

5. **Think about possible obstacles and how to overcome them.** Changing a well-established habit is a journey full of obstacles. Unfortunately, when we hit some of these, we often quit. As you plan to make a change now, think it through, and anticipate your obstacles. Make a clear plan to overcome these expected rough spots in your journey.

6. **Develop an easy method to measure progress.** You can change habits without keeping a log, but a log just increases your chances of success. Research shows that keeping track of what you do increases your chance of success significantly. Keeping track helps you be consistent and creates awareness of what you're actually doing. It can motivate you and tell your history of success!

7. **Create a way to be accountable to others and to yourself.** Sometimes it is easier to be accountable to others, and we can talk ourselves into almost anything. It is harder to make excuses, if you have publicly committed to a change. Create an accountability mechanism that will help you make the change you desire in your life.

8. **Know the triggers that can derail your change.** When you are trying to change a habit, such as stress eating, it is essential to find out what causes you to behave in the way you want to change. This is an important key to changing habits. Unless you identify these triggers and learn to neutralize their effect, they can derail your success. Be honest with yourself in identifying these triggers. There is no right or wrong, just data, that you can analyze and make a plan to modify as needed. Being prepared will give you more options, and a higher chance for success.

9. **Keep your focus on the desired outcome**. Focus will help you be consistent and ready for the long run required for changes. It is important to know that it will take some time to develop a new habit. When you stick to this new desired habit for at least 30 days, you will have a much better chance to reach sustainable change.

10. **Be prepared to "stay the course for the long run" and embrace failure as learning opportunities**. Change does not happen overnight, and it is important that you understand that giving up on your dream will not be a good option! Be prepared to start over if you are not successful the first time you try to change a habit. This is not a sprint, or even a marathon, but a lifelong process. Don't give up. Just figure out why you missed, and plan to beat that obstacle next time. Then be as consistent as possible from then on out, until the habit is ingrained. Be the captain of your life and learn from the failures. When you do this, you can reset your resolve, learn from your experience, and allow the failure to become the force that helps you succeed. This quote from Anthony J. D'Angelo—a young man who had a vision to improve higher education in this country—says it all! *"In order to succeed you must fail, so that you know what not to do the next time."*

> *"We are what we repeatedly do.*
> *Excellence then, is not an act, but a habit."*
> Aristotle

The Wheel of Your Life

As you get ready for your journey of transformation, here is a tool that can help you determine where you are right now in various areas of your life that are important to you.

*The **Wheel of Life** is a great way to give you a snapshot of your present. And it offers an opportunity to identify those areas that may need some focus and attention.*

Instructions to complete this exercise:

- Get a blank sheet of paper.
- Draw a large circle.
- Divide the circle into 8 segments – like a pizza – where each piece represents an area of your life as it is now.

Label each segment with eight (8) aspects that are important to you in your life, such as health, career, relationships, personal development, work, leisure.

Here is an example of the Wheel of Life showing eight (8) key areas of life:

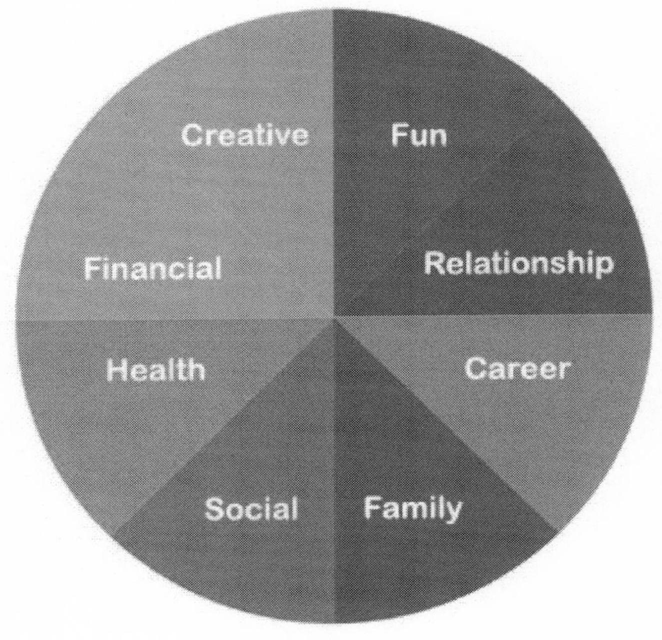

You can use these labels or, if there is a specific area of your life you would like to examine just substitute a category. Create categories that are meaningful to you.

The general categories include:

Fun - Happiness, Hobbies

Relationships – Important People in Your Life.

Career – Job Satisfaction, Career Path.

Family – Children, Parents, Siblings, Relatives

Social – Friends, Sports, Other Activities

Health – Exercise, Nutrition, Physical Self-care

Financial – Savings, Investments

Creative – Self-space, Spiritual Life, Artistic

How to complete the Wheel:

Assign a number from 1 to 10 next to each category in the wheel, as follows: write 1 if you are unsatisfied in this area and up to 10 if you are totally satisfied.

____

____

____

____

____

____.

Looking at your scores, which are the two (2) lowest scores? Take time to consider what these mean to you and your life.

____

____

____

____

____.

Based on what you have learned from completing the Wheel of Life, which are the two (2) areas you would like to move forward? Select what makes more sense to you at this time. It does not have to be the two (2) lowest scores.

Moving forward:

____

____

____

____

____

____

____.

Use the information to work your plan of personal transformation. How would you feel if you could significantly move forward in the two (2) areas you have selected?

____

____

____

____

____

____

____.

Describe below what would change for you, and what this would mean for your life.

Action

____

____

____

____

____

____.

What could you do to start moving forward in these areas? List at least 2 concrete actions you can take to make the changes you want.

____

____

____

____

____.

Use the workbook to record your insights based on this exercise.

____

____

____

____

____.

12 Habits of Happy People

Happiness is a state of mind and you can create a more positive reality for yourself by using some of the suggestions below.

1. **Act** happy – even if you don't feel it. A smile gets other smiles, which makes a lightened happy heart.
2. Enjoy the **moment**. Happiness is seeing the wonder and recognizing the special things that are happening every moment. Smell the roses, talk to a tree.
3. Get **outside**. Is it daytime? Step outside and look at the sky and clouds. Is it nigh time? Check out the stars and the moon. Is it raining? Put your hand out of the window to feel the raindrops on your fingertips.
4. Take control of your **time**. Set little goals for each day.
5. Take regular **exercise** – proven to be as effective in treating depression as medication.
6. Get **rest**. Take it easy, learn how to relax and let go. Allow time for enough sleep and time out to recharge your batteries.
7. **Whistle** your way through life – or sing a silly tune! At the least, smile ☺ **!**
8. Pat your **pet**.
9. Feed your **soul** – with a good book, an inspiring read or do some "positive surfing" on the web – Keywords: Happy, Joy,
10. Make time for and invest in close nurturing **relationships**. Call a friend or family member or get together for a coffee.
11. **Get out** of a rut. Change something. Go somewhere new. Go to the country or the beach and feel the sand between your toes. If you can't go just imagine it and you will smile!
12. Finally – Do you want to be happy? Whatever you give you will yourself receive, so **give what you would like to receive**. If you want to be happy, do something for others that makes them happy, and **you** will be happy.

Action:

Identify 3 things that make you happy and commit to do at least one of these every day.

The Five Stages of Grief

Letting go of the past involves a process of grief, and grief occurs as the result of the loss of something that has an important meaning for you. The common factor when one loses something of importance is change. Change, even positive change, equates to loss and any loss requires an adjustment – this adjustment process is felt as grief.

An awareness of the stages of grief can help to deal with the feelings that inevitably accompany loss. When one develops the awareness of such feelings as normal, and recognizable as part of the change, only then is the process allowed to work.

As we are all different, it is important to remember that people can experience the stages in varying orders, times or degrees of intensity.

The Five Stages of Grief, identified by Dr. Elizabeth Kübler-Ross in 1969 are described below:

Denial

This first stage in the grief process is a natural reaction to unexpected change. At this stage, we cannot accept that the change or loss has actually occurred. We want to believe that our reality has not been altered.

Anger

When denial is no longer possible, the next stage is anger, especially towards those closest to us and common questions include: *"Why me? It's not fair!" "How can this happen to me?" "Who is to blame?" "It should not be happening."*

Bargaining & Regret

The third stage involves the hope that we will be able to avoid the cause of the grief. It is a time for negotiations with a Higher Power, compromises and bargaining. We are trying to come to terms with what has happened and may regret what we didn't or could not do. Common thoughts include: *"If only ... "I wish ... "Maybe if ...."*

Sadness

Feelings of sadness actually signal the end of the grieving process. Sadness is a very positive emotion. It means we are beginning to actually **feel** the loss and come to terms with it. We may wish to end this stage and to "move on" as quickly as possible, but at such times it is good to recall the medical maxim, "*Patients need patience*."

Acceptance

The final stage in the first cycle of grief is acceptance and represents that the healing is underway. We are starting to incorporate the knowledge that the change is now real and a part of our reality, into our life and our thinking.

Awareness of the stages of grief can help to give ourselves permission to grieve and heal. It can also increase our emotional competence because we are better able to identify what we are feeling and why.

Morning Pages

In her book – **The Artist's Way: A Spiritual Path to Higher Creativity** – Julia Cameron introduces the idea of "Morning Pages" as a powerful tool to move your thoughts into actions. She describes this process as a way to clear your mind and retrain its focus. You may want to try and see how this works for you!

Below is Julia Cameron's own description of her process:

> *There's a time every morning when we are half awake, half asleep and not quite fully conscious. At those moments, we have access to our unconscious mind and our inner workings. But like dew on the morning grass, it will soon be gone without a trace. Listening to these tender morning wisps allows us to reach into our inner world, the deeper part of ourselves that helps guide us on our path of transformation.*
>
> *Early morning pages are a stream of consciousness written in a journal first thing in the morning. Keep your journal by your bed and reach for it while you are still half asleep.*

1. *Begin by writing down any memories you may have of your dreams. At first there may be nothing, or simply minor recollections, but as you do this over and over you will build the muscle. You'll send a powerful message to your brain: I am prepared to accept my unconscious thoughts and feelings, and I accept that more and more will be revealed. You will develop a deep, direct relationship with your inner self.*

2. *Next, write 10 things you are grateful for from yesterday. Usually our minds focus on everything that's not going well, skipping over the fact that we live in a peaceful, democratic country. Your mind easily forgets that you have great friends, a place to live, plenty of food to eat, access to education, a job and freedom. Take time for thanksgiving and appreciating what went well yesterday.*

3. *Next comes the stream of consciousness writing. Write for at least a page, maybe two. Write whatever crosses your mind. Nothing is too petty, too bad or too silly to write down. Nobody will be reading this, so write it all. No censoring. You will be amazed at what comes out of your sweet, innocent mind. Write quickly or write slowly. Find a pace that works for you.*

   All the angry, ugly stuff that you write in the morning would otherwise stand in the way of you being your best you. By doing early morning pages, you get all those repressed thoughts out of your system so you can live your life and realize that you are not your mind and you are not your thoughts. You are a spiritual being in a material world, moving forward toward the life you deserve, which is the life you truly came here to live.

   Watch your breath. Watch your mind. It's like a meditation. Be still and just let it all pass from your mind onto the paper.

Made in the USA
Monee, IL
09 February 2020